Guitar Tablature Edition

C000089690

1977

Island Music Limited

Guitar Tablature Explained

Guitar Music can be notated three different ways: on a *musical stave*, in *tablature*, and in *rhythm slashes*

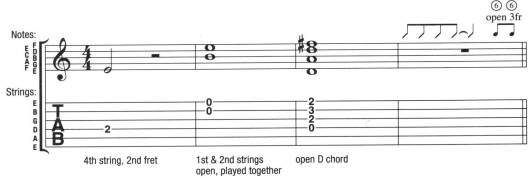

RHYTHM SLASHES are written above the stave. Strum chords in the rhythm indicated. Round noteheads indicate single notes.

THE MUSICAL STAVE shows pitches and rhythms and is divided by lines into bars. Pitches are named after the first seven letters of the alphabet.

TABLATURE graphically represents the guitar fingerboard. Each horizontal line represents a string, and each number represents a fret.

4th string, 2nd fret   1st & 2nd strings open, played together   open D chord

Definitions for Special Guitar Notation

SEMI-TONE BEND: Strike the note and bend up a semi-tone (1/2 step).

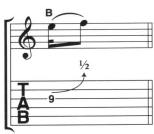

WHOLE-TONE BEND: Strike the note and bend up a whole-tone (whole step).

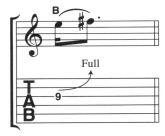

GRACE NOTE BEND: Strike the note and bend as indicated. Play the first note as quickly as possible.

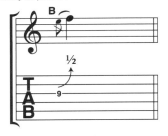

QUARTER-TONE BEND: Strike the note and bend up a 1/4 step.

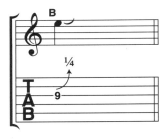

BEND & RELEASE: Strike the note and bend up as indicated, then release back to the original note.

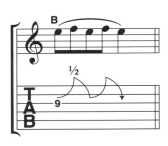

COMPOUND BEND & RELEASE: Strike the note and bend up and down in the rhythm indicated.

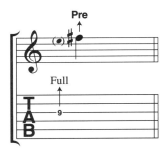

PRE-BEND: Bend the note as indicated, then strike it.

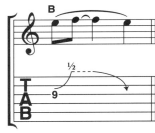

PRE-BEND & RELEASE: Bend the note as indicated. Strike it and release the note back to the original pitch.

UNISON BEND: Strike the two notes simultaneously and bend the lower note up to the pitch of the higher.

BEND & RESTRIKE: Strike the note and bend as indicated then restrike the string where the symbol occurs.

BEND, HOLD AND RELEASE: Same as bend and release but hold the bend for the duration of the tie.

BEND AND TAP: Bend the note as indicated and tap the higher fret while still holding the bend.

VIBRATO: The string is vibrated by rapidly bending and releasing the note with the fretting hand.

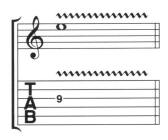

HAMMER-ON: Strike the first (lower) note with one finger, then sound the higher note (on the same string) with another finger by fretting it without picking.

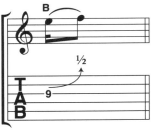

PULL-OFF: Place both fingers on the notes to be sounded, Strike the first note and without picking, pull the finger off to sound the second (lower) note.

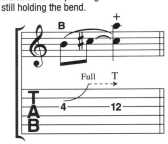

LEGATO SLIDE (GLISS): Strike the first note and then slide the same fret-hand finger up or down to the second note. The second note is not struck.

NOTE: The speed of any bend is indicated by the music notation and tempo.

SHIFT SLIDE (GLISS & RESTRIKE): Same as legato slide, except the second note is struck.

TRILL: Very rapidly alternate between the notes indicated by continuously hammering on and pulling off.

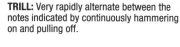

TAPPING: Hammer ("tap") the fret indicated with the pick-hand index or middle finger and pull off to the note fretted by the fret hand.

PICK SCRAPE: The edge of the pick is rubbed down (or up) the string, producing a scratchy sound.

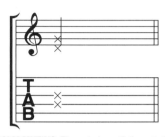

MUFFLED STRINGS: A percussive sound is produced by laying the fret hand across the string(s) without depressing, and striking them with the pick hand.

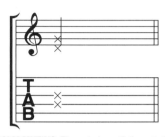

NATURAL HARMONIC: Strike the note while the fret-hand lightly touches the string directly over the fret indicated.

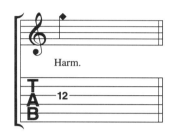

PINCH HARMONIC: The note is fretted normally and a harmonic is produced by adding the edge of the thumb or the tip of the index finger of the pick hand to the normal pick attack.

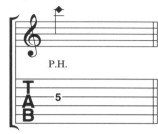

HARP HARMONIC: The note is fretted normally and a harmonic is produced by gently resting the pick hand's index finger directly above the indicated fret (in parentheses) while the pick hand's thumb or pick assists by plucking the appropriate string.

PALM MUTING: The note is partially muted by the pick hand lightly touching the string(s) just before the bridge.

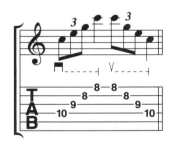

RAKE: Drag the pick across the strings indicated with a single motion.

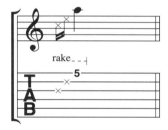

TREMOLO PICKING: The note is picked as rapidly and continuously as possible.

ARPEGGIATE: Play the notes of the chord indicated by quickly rolling them from bottom to top.

SWEEP PICKING: Rhythmic downstroke and/or upstroke motion across the strings.

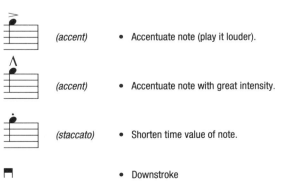

VIBRATO DIVE BAR AND RETURN: The pitch of the note or chord is dropped a specific number of steps (in rhythm) then returned to the original pitch.

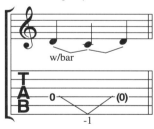

VIBRATO BAR SCOOP: Depress the bar just before striking the note, then quickly release the bar.

VIBRATO BAR DIP: Strike the note and then immediately drop a specific number of steps, then release back to the original pitch.

Additional Musical Definitions

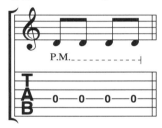 (accent)	• Accentuate note (play it louder).	

(accent) • Accentuate note with great intensity.

(staccato) • Shorten time value of note.

■ • Downstroke

V • Upstroke

D.%. al Coda

• Go back to the sign (%), then play until the bar marked *To Coda* ⊕ then skip to the section marked ⊕ *Coda*.

D.C. al Fine

• Go back to the beginning of the song and play until the bar marked *Fine* (end).

tacet

• Instrument is silent (drops out).

• Repeat bars between signs.

1.	2.

• When a repeated section has different endings, play the first ending only the first time and the second ending only the second time.

NOTE: Tablature numbers in parentheses mean: 1. The note is sustained, but a new articulation (such as hammer on or slide) begins.
2. A note may be fretted but not necessarily played.

Lose Control

Words & Music by Mark Hamilton & Tim Wheeler

2. Chorus

Here comes the night,___ it is com - ing on,___ the lights are low___

and the re - cord's on,___ in - side your veins___ and you lead me on,___

here comes the night,___ it is com - ing on.

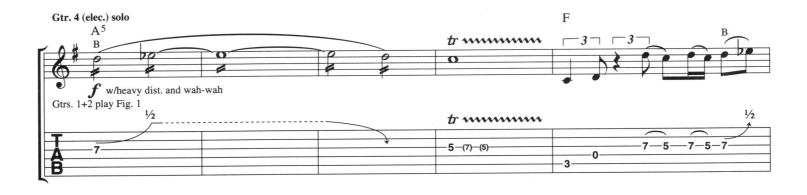

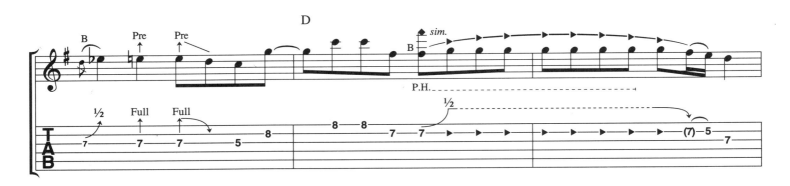

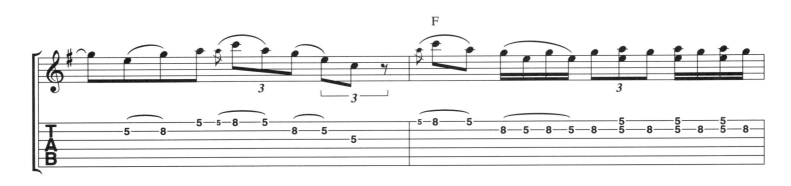

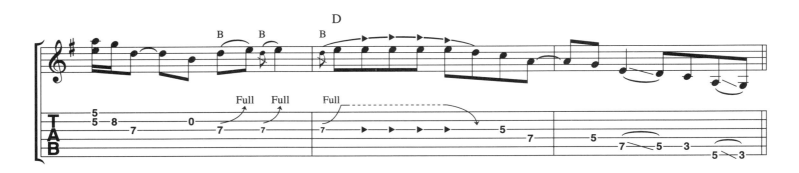

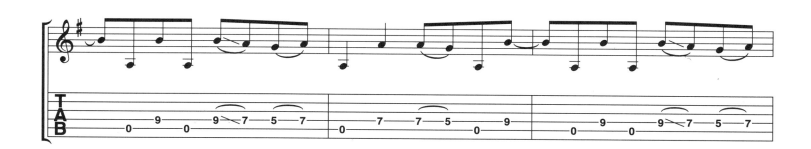

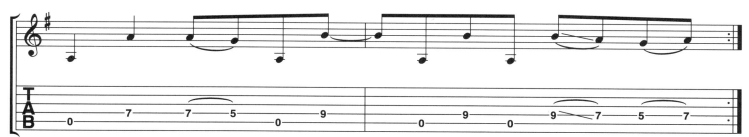

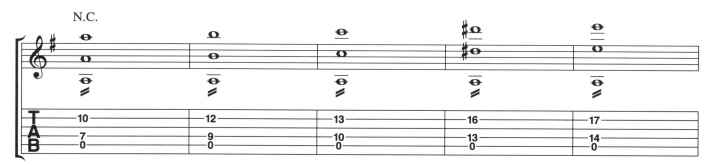

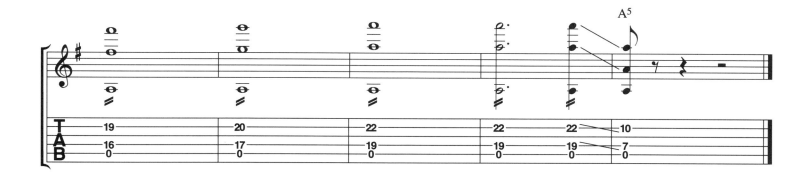

11

Goldfinger

Words & Music by Tim Wheeler

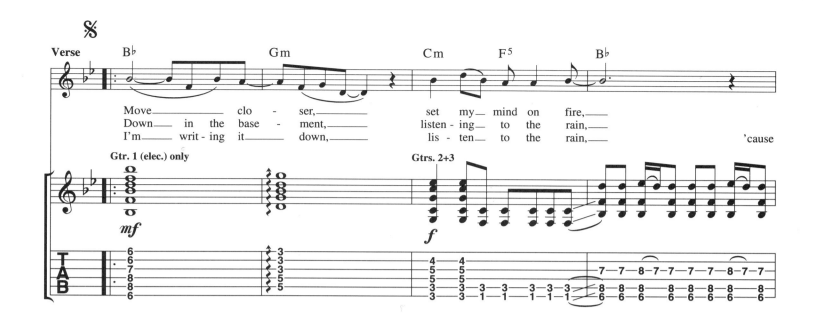

Verse

Move——— clo - ser,——— set my— mind on fire,———
Down——— in the base - ment,——— listen - ing— to the rain,———
I'm——— writ - ing it— down,——— lis - ten— to the rain,——— 'cause

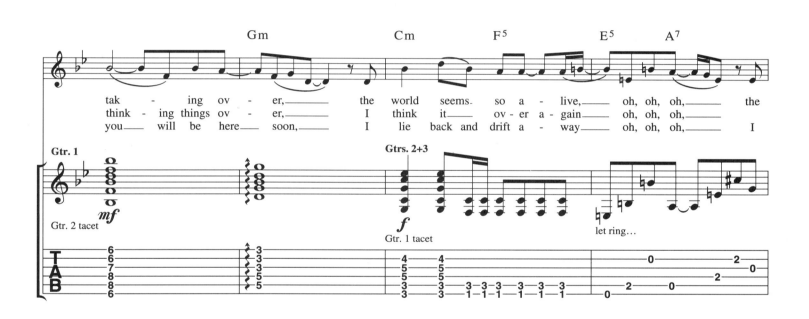

tak - ing ov - er,——— the world seems— so a - live,——— oh, oh, oh,——— the
think - ing things ov - er,——— I think it— ov - er a - gain——— oh, oh, oh,——— the
you—— will be here—— soon,——— I lie back and drift a - way——— oh, oh, oh,——— I

world seems— so a - live.———
think it— ov - er a - gain.———
lie back and drift a - way.——— She slips in - to the night,—
She slipped in - to the night,—
She slipped in - to the night,—

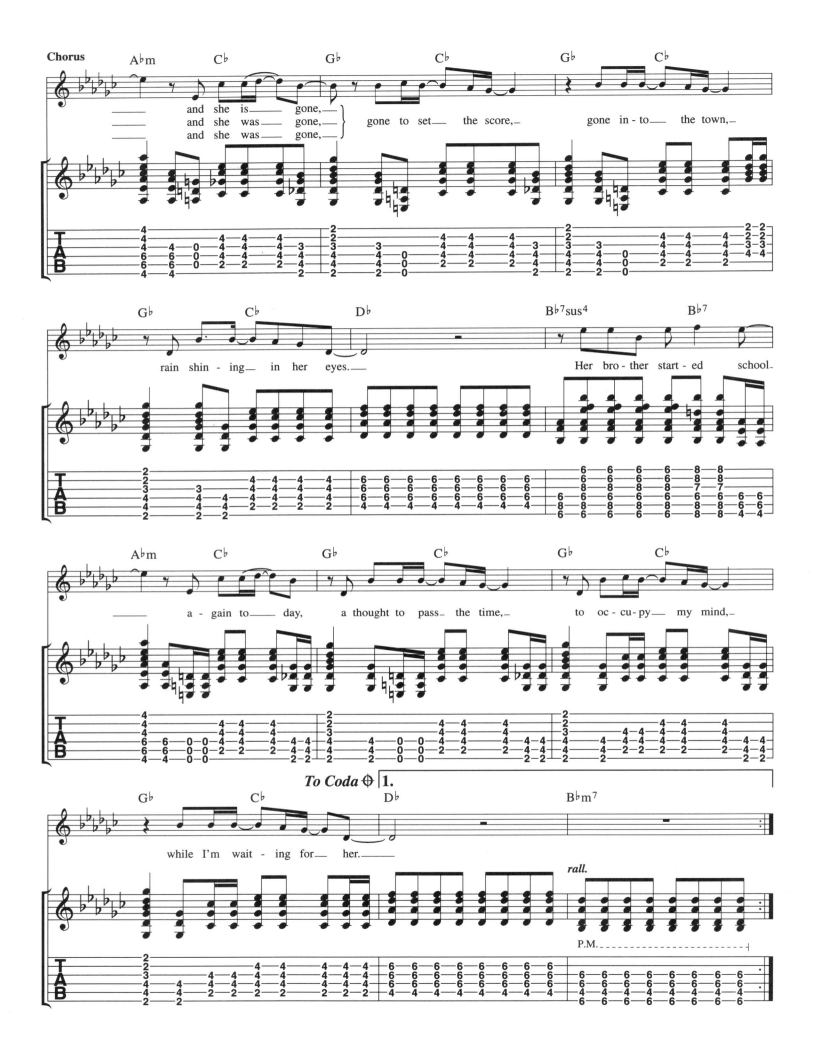

Chorus

and she is gone,
and she was gone,
and she was gone,

gone to set the score,

gone in-to the town,

rain shin-ing in her eyes.

Her bro-ther start-ed school

a - gain to day,

a thought to pass the time,

to oc-cu-py my mind,

To Coda ⊕ **1.**

while I'm wait - ing for her.

rall.

P.M.

14

15

Girl From Mars

Words & Music by Tim Wheeler

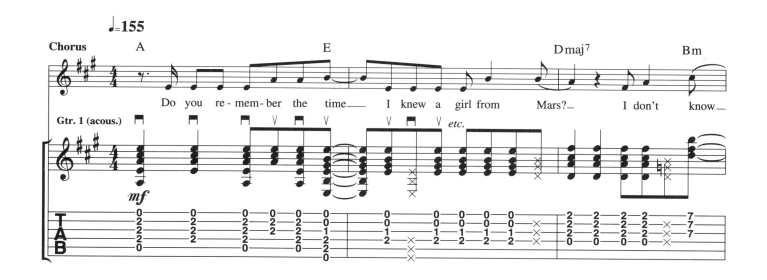

Chorus

Do you re - mem - ber the time___ I knew a girl from Mars?___ I don't know___

Gtr. 1 (acous.)

___ if you knew___ that. Oh, we'd stay up late play - ing cards,___ Hen - ry Win - ter - man ci -

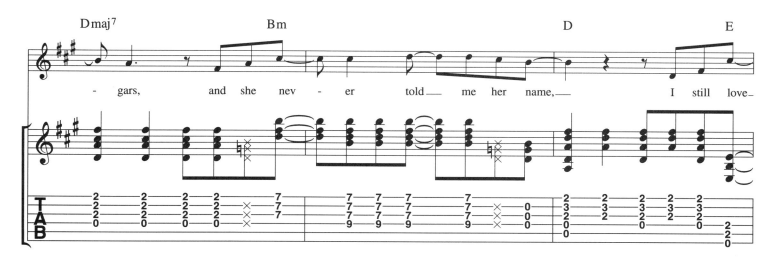

- gars, and she nev - er told___ me her name,___ I still love___

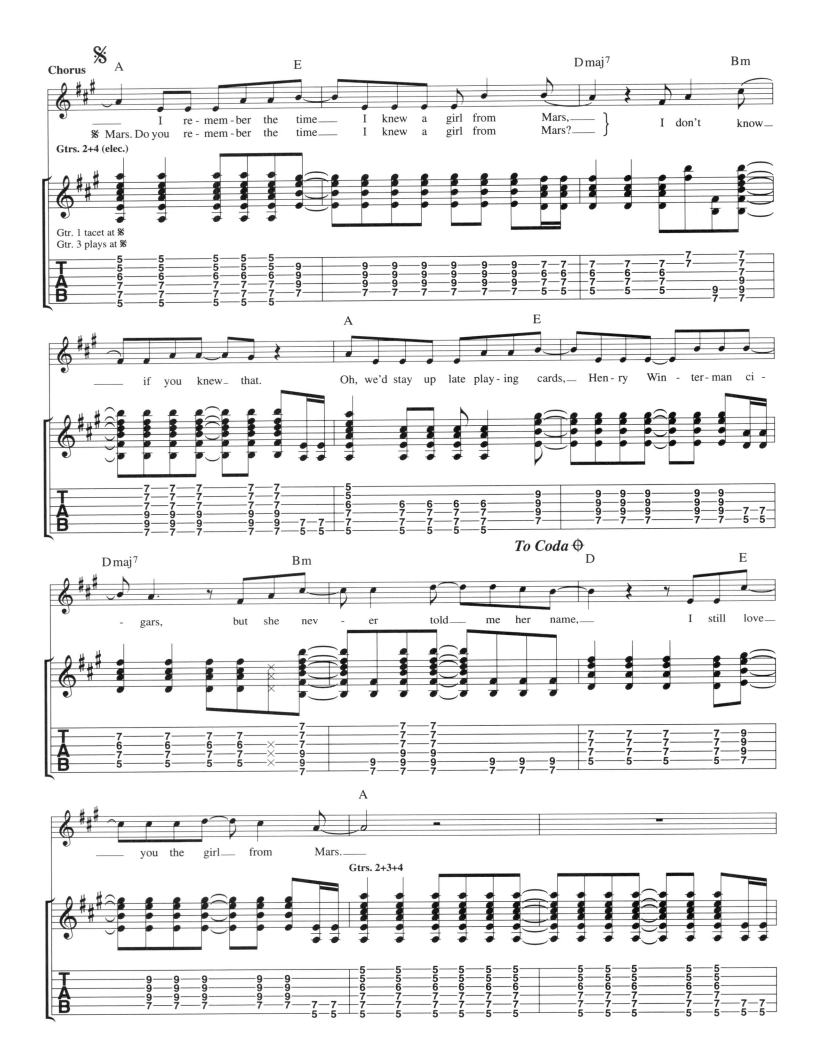

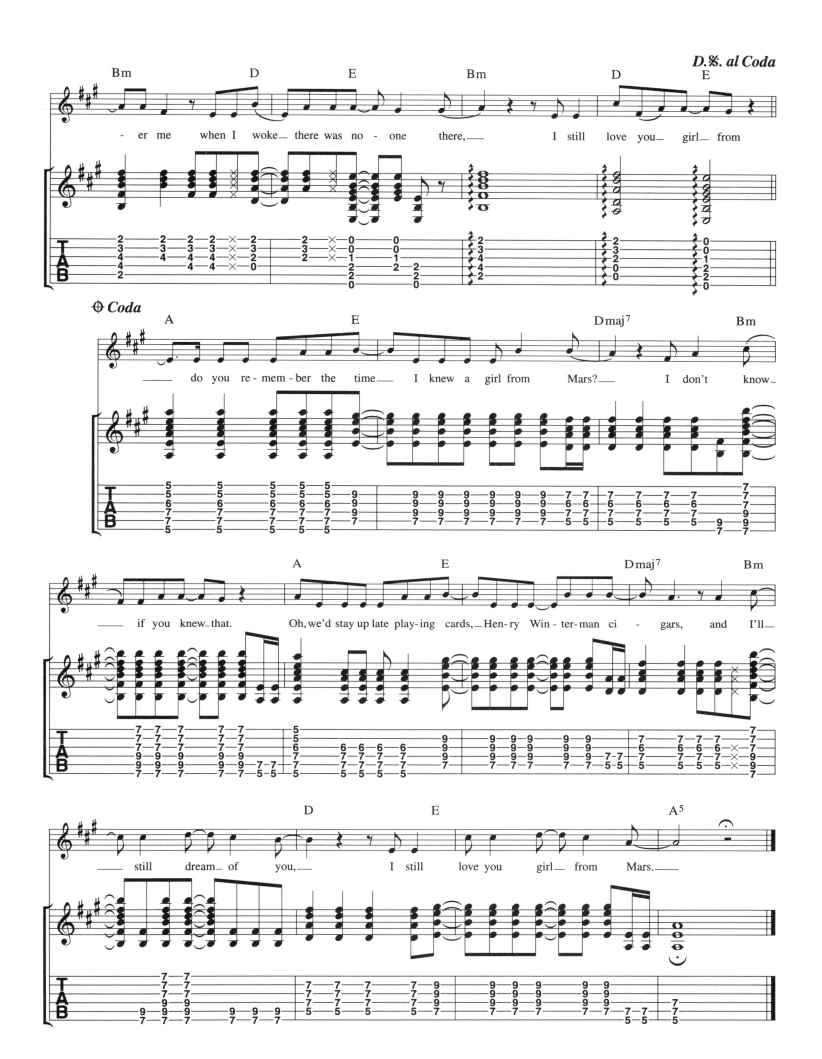

I'd Give You Anything
Words & Music by Tim Wheeler

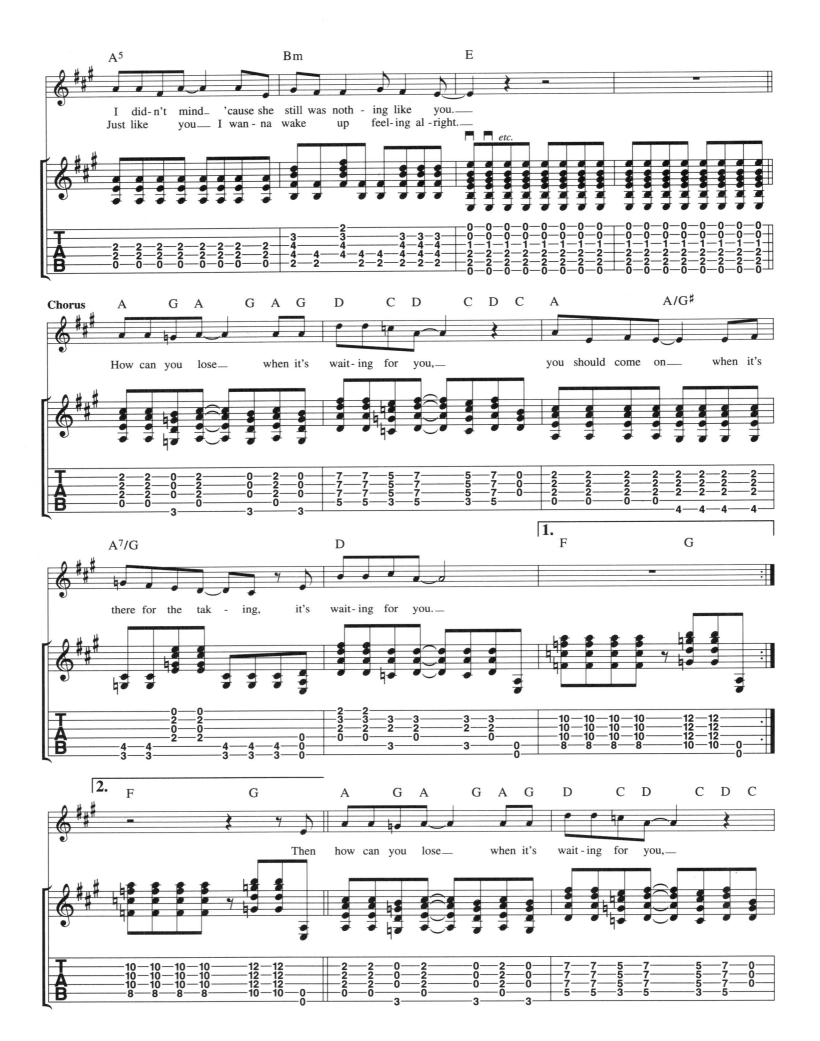

Gone The Dream

Words & Music by Tim Wheeler

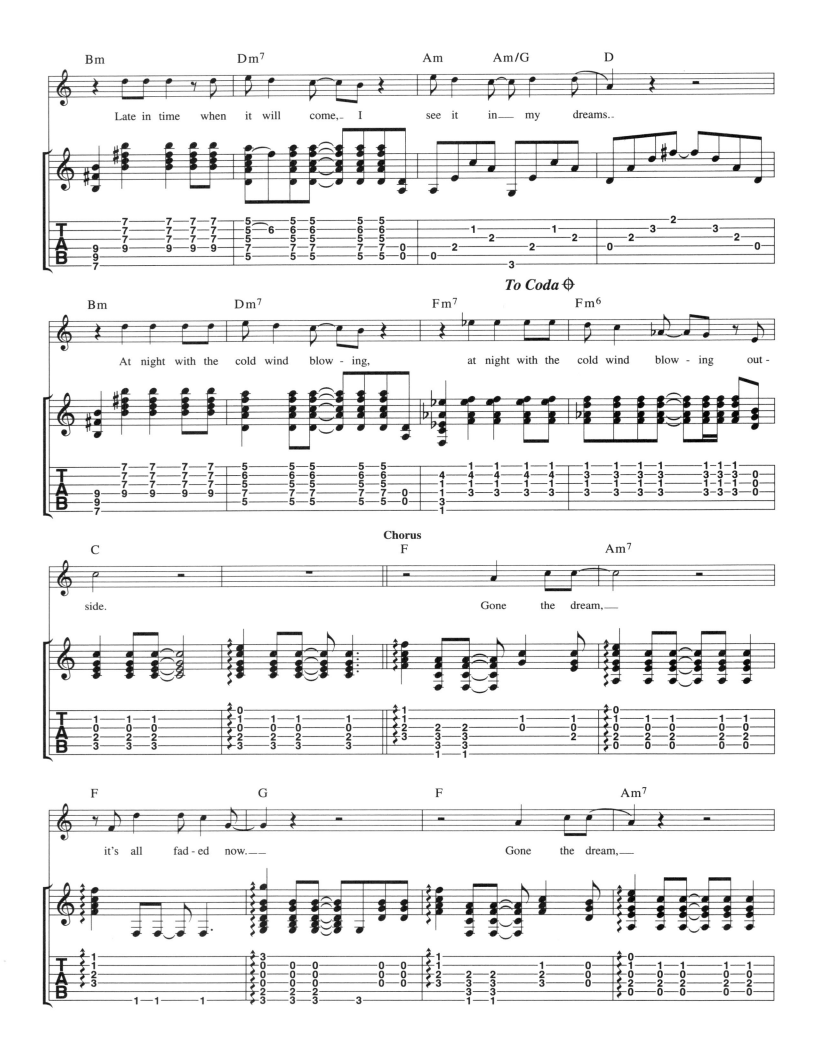

Kung Fu

Words & Music by Tim Wheeler

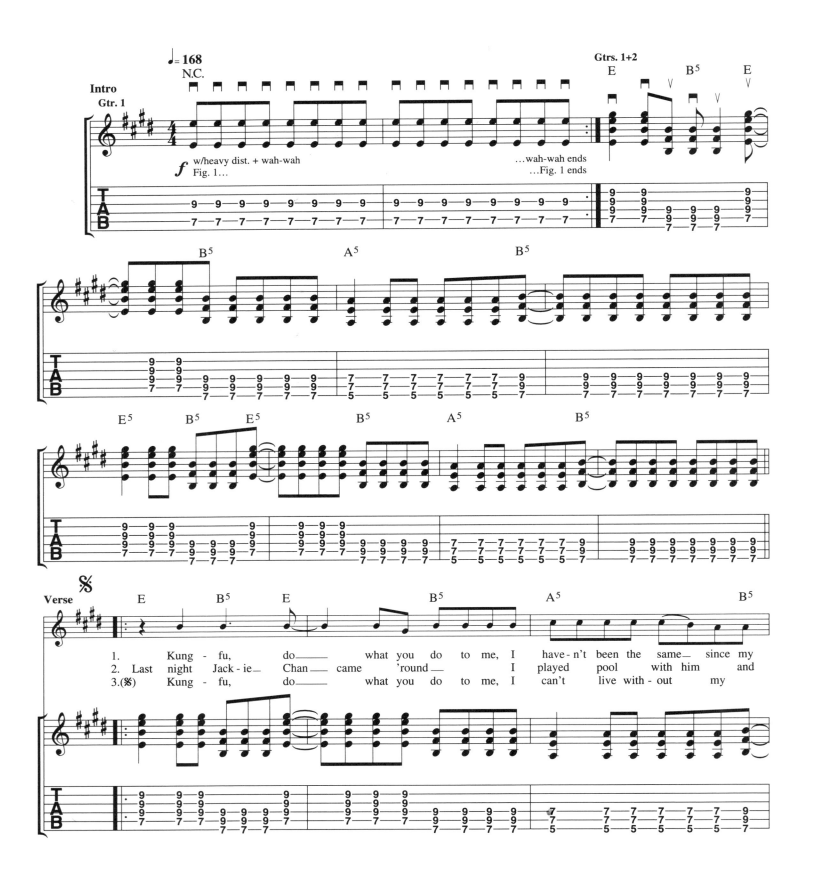

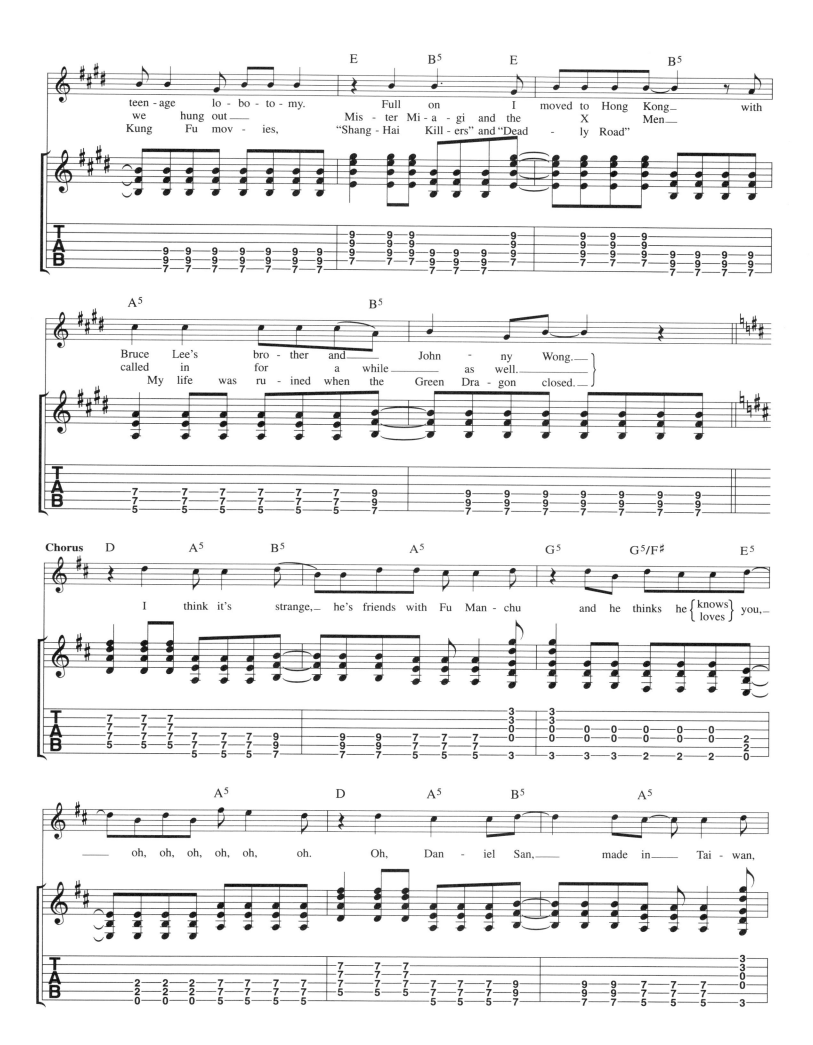

33

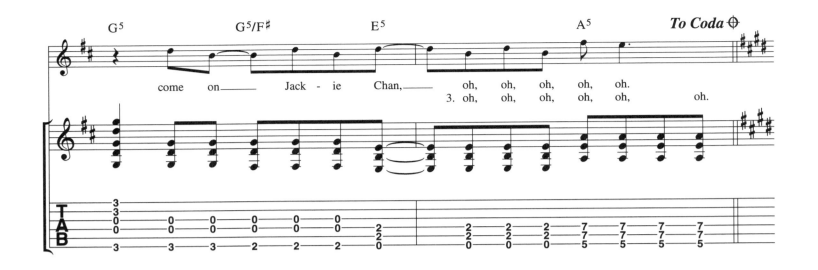

come on____ Jack - ie Chan,____ oh, oh, oh, oh, oh.
3. oh, oh, oh, oh, oh, oh.

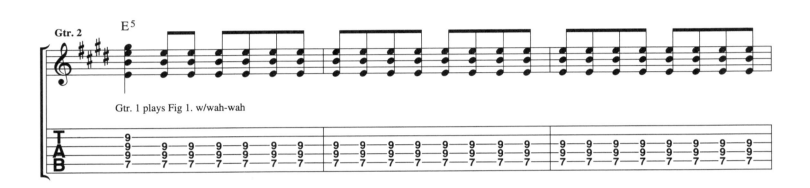

Gtr. 2

Gtr. 1 plays Fig 1. w/wah-wah

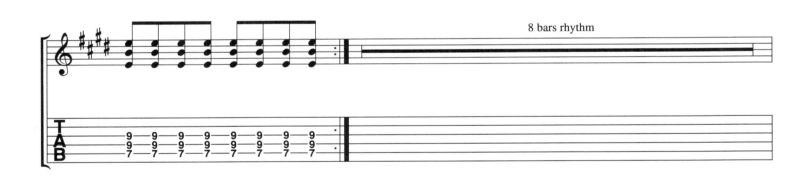

8 bars rhythm

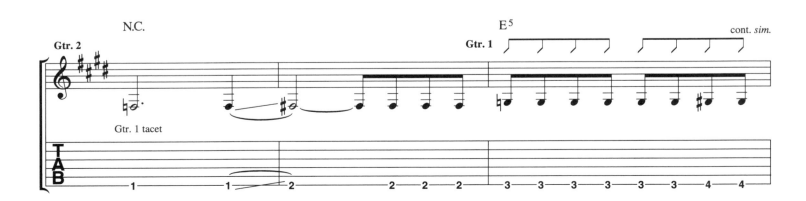

Gtr. 2

N.C.

Gtr. 1 tacet

E⁵

Gtr. 1

cont. *sim.*

35

Oh Yeah

Words & Music by Tim Wheeler

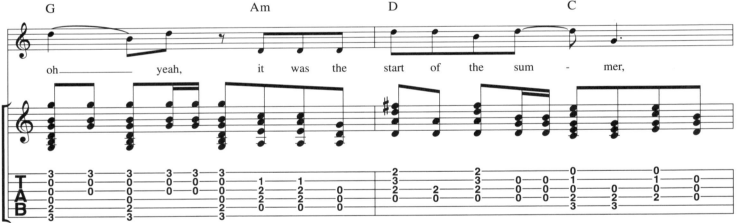

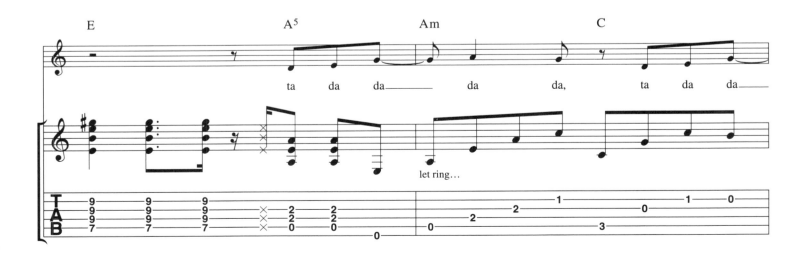

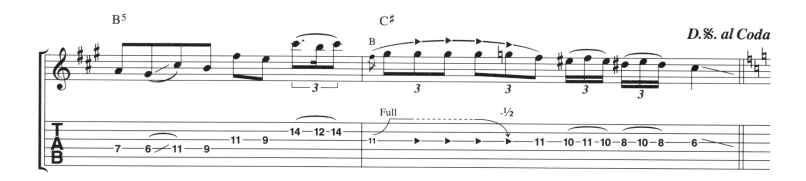

⊕ *Coda*

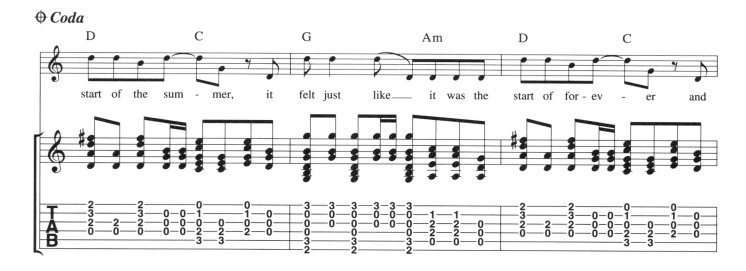

start of the sum - mer,   it   felt just   like___ it was the   start of for - ev - er   and

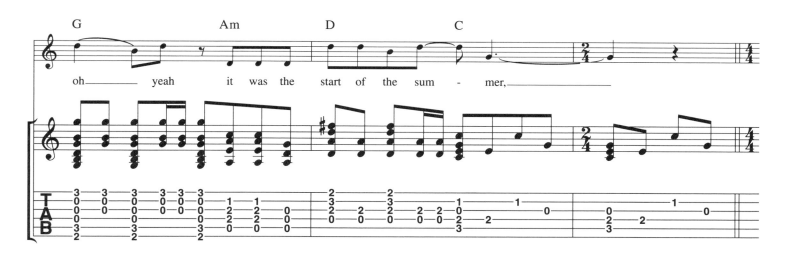

oh_____ yeah   it was the   start of the sum - mer,_____

ooh,   ah,   ooh,_____ ah.

rall.

Let It Flow

Words & Music by Tim Wheeler

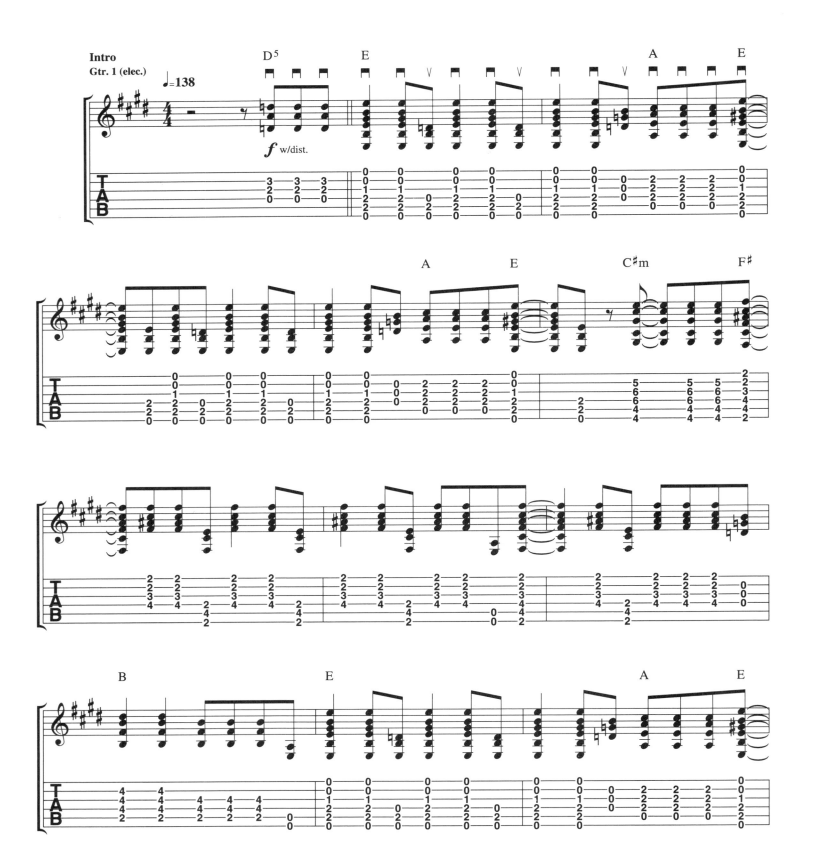

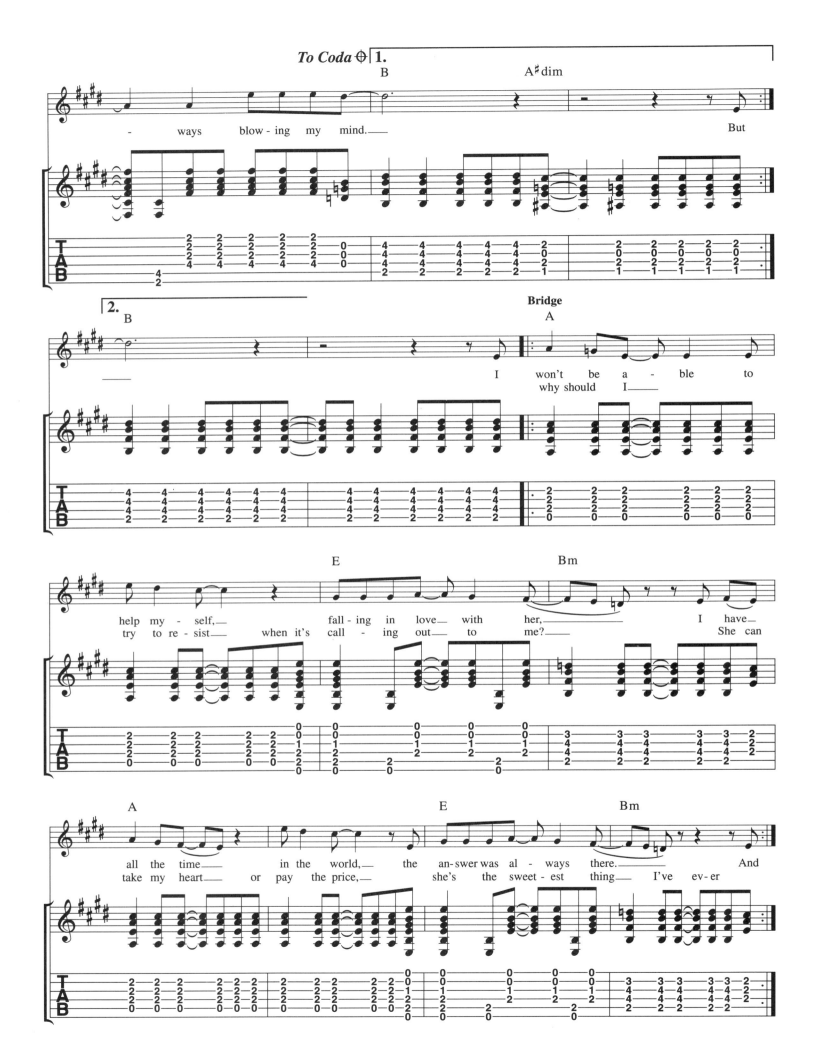

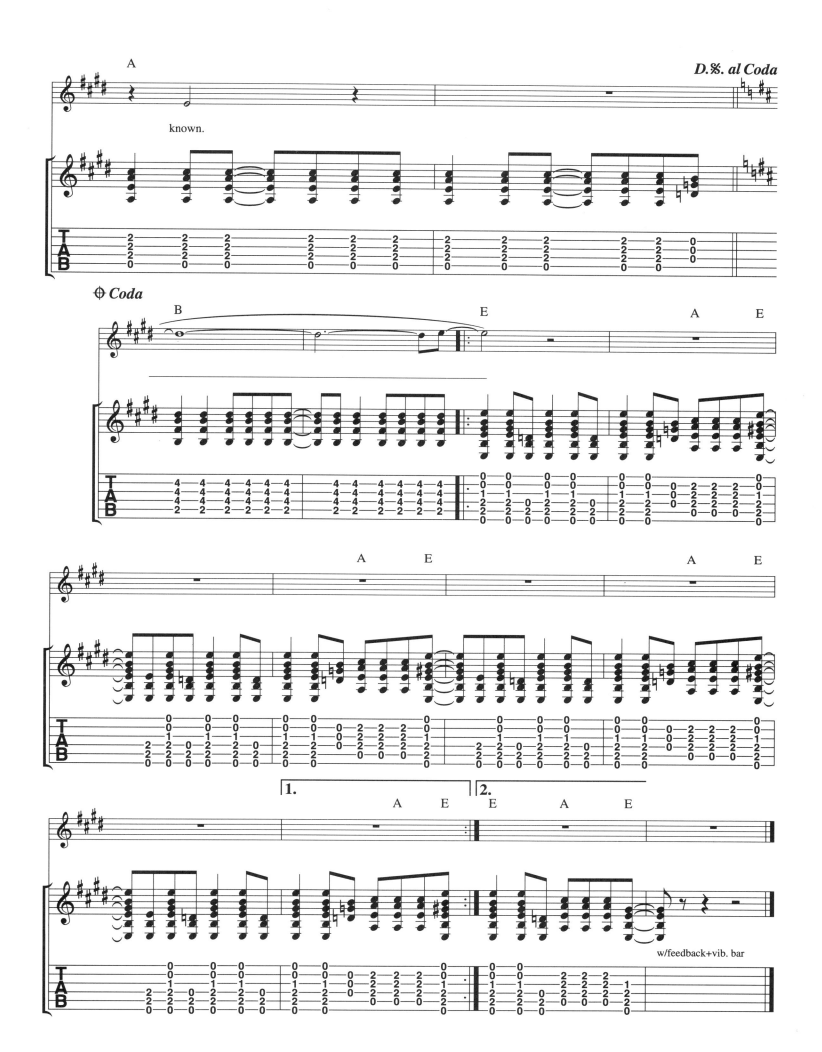

Angel Interceptor

Words & Music by Tim Wheeler & Rick McMurray

51

Lost In You

Words & Music by Tim Wheeler

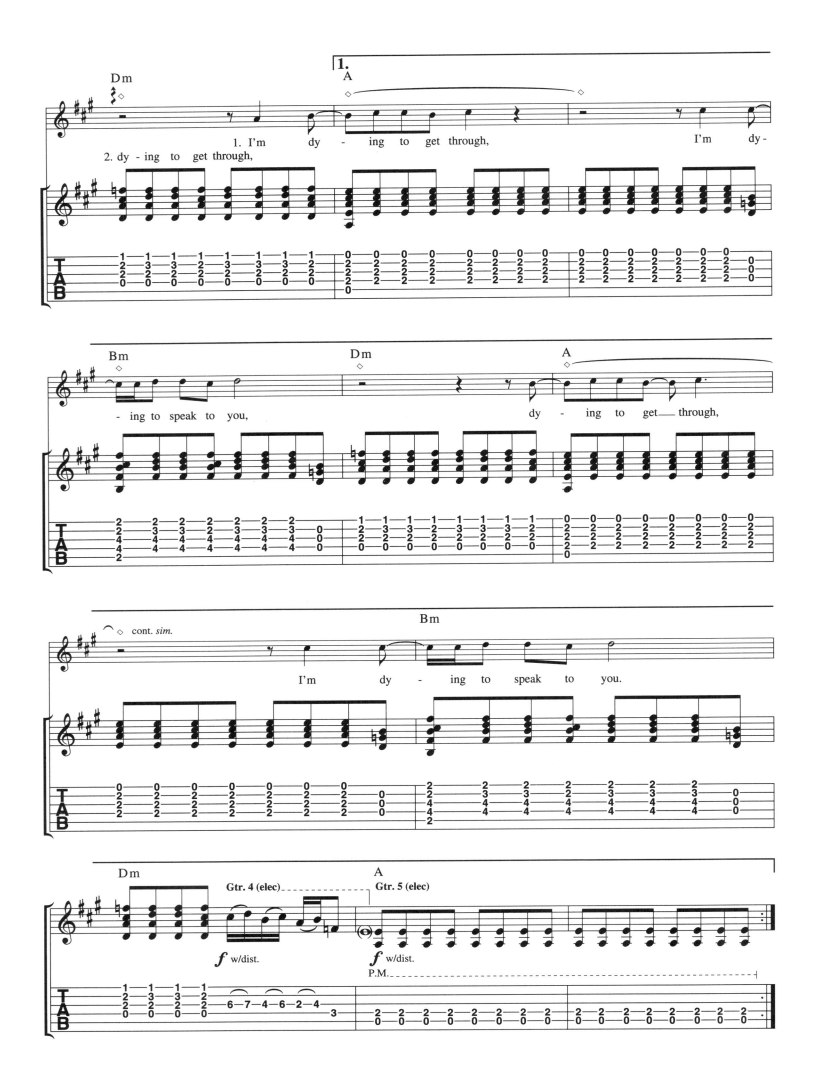

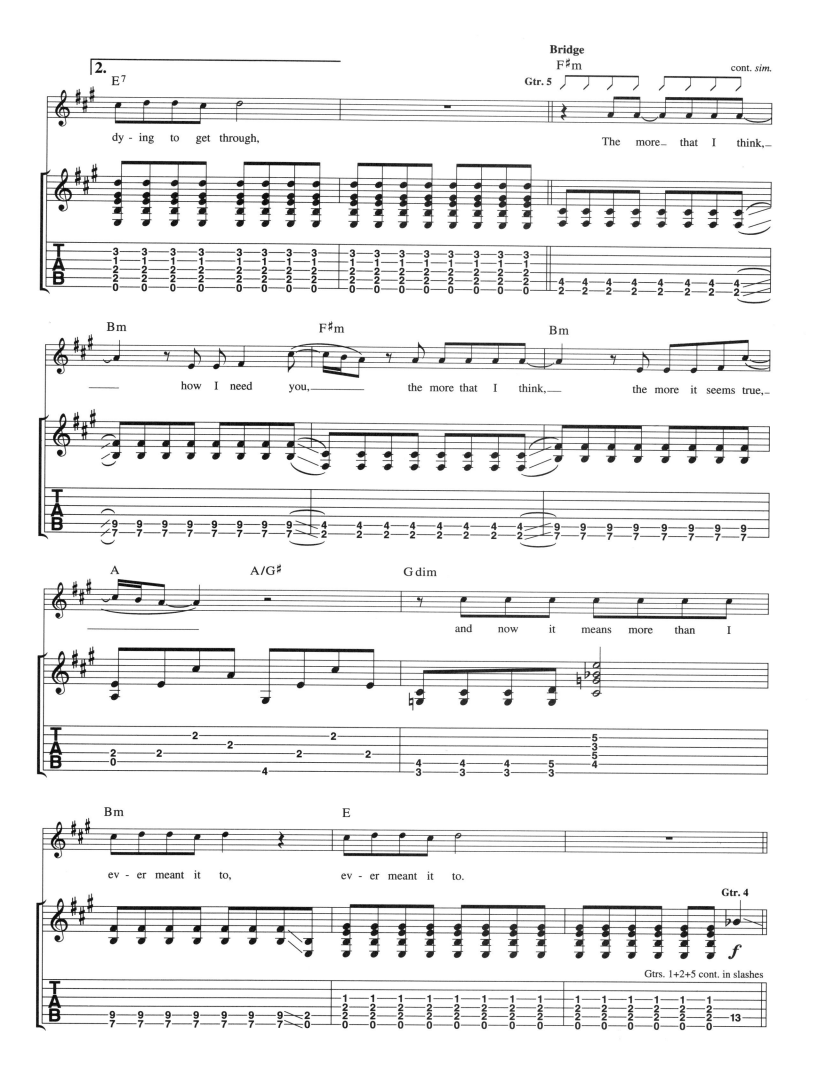

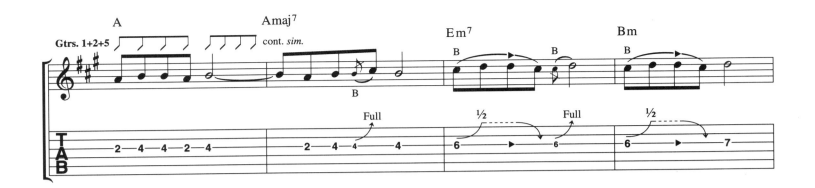

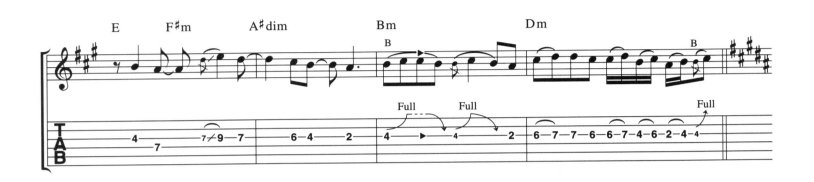

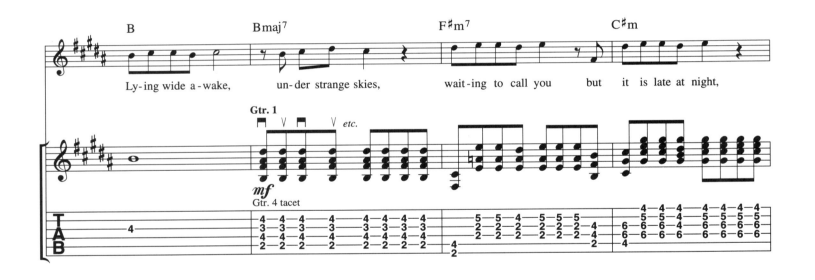

Ly-ing wide a-wake,   un-der strange skies,   wait-ing to call you   but   it is late at night,

and you're far—— a - way—— but you—— are   al-ways on my mind,

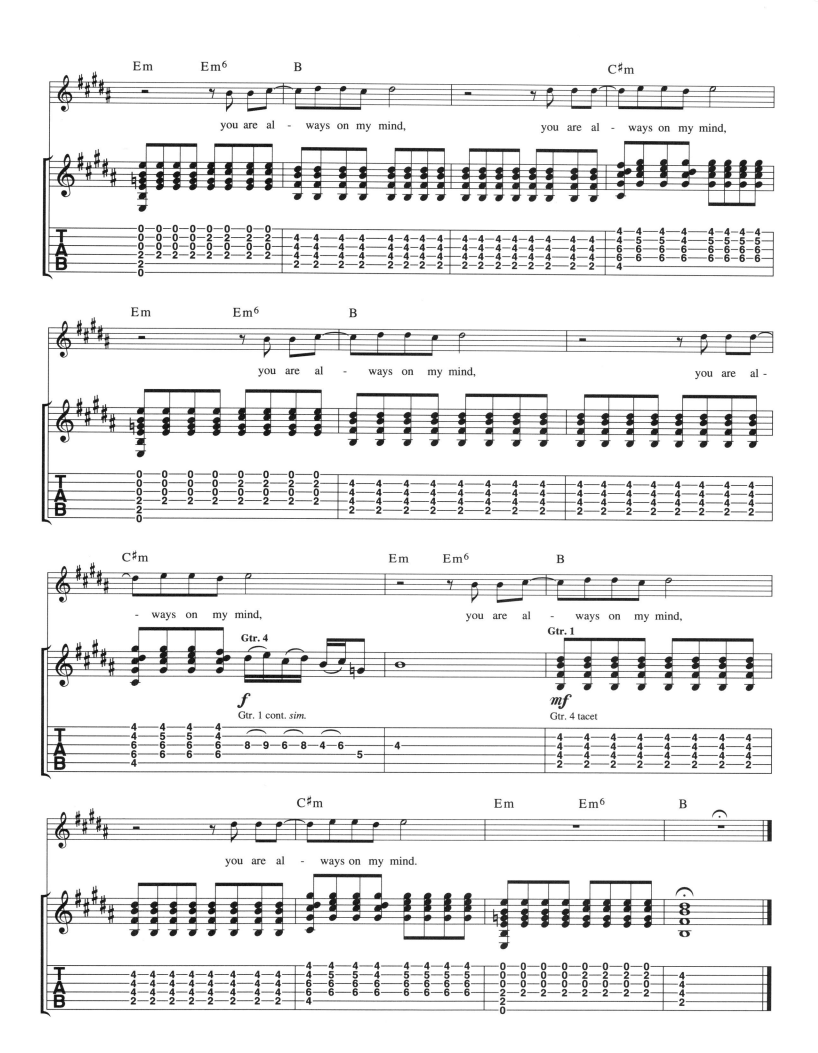

Innocent Smile

Words & Music by Mark Hamilton

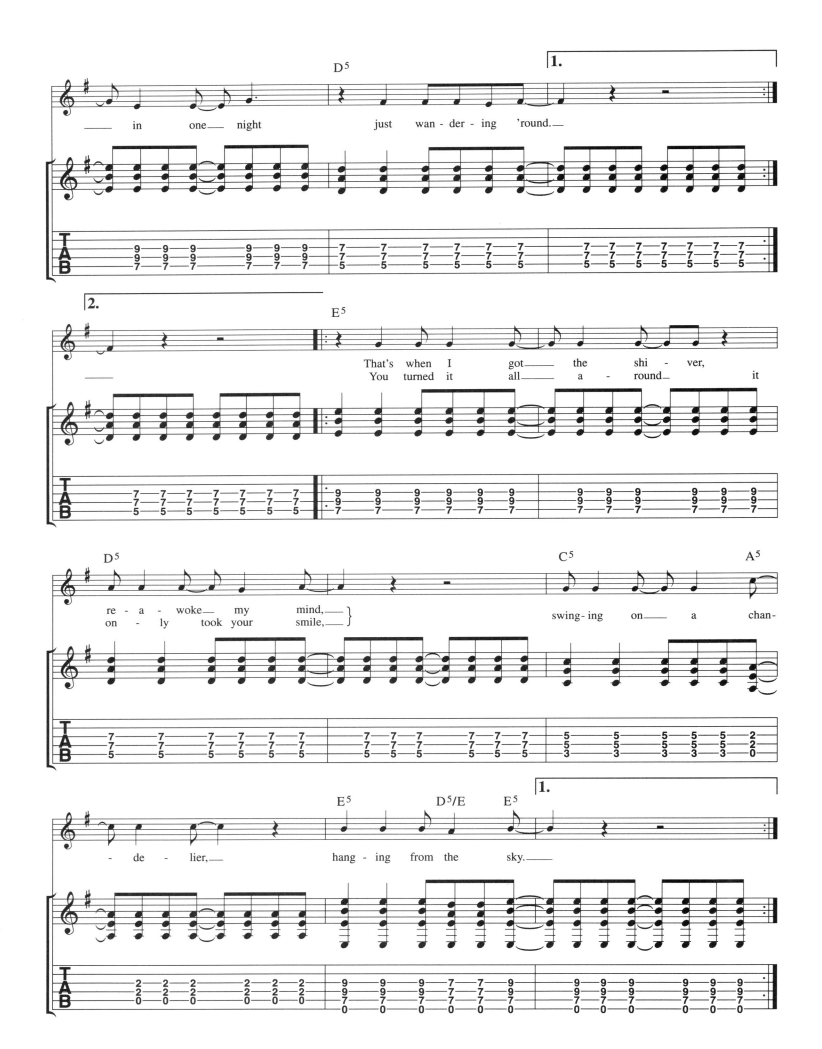

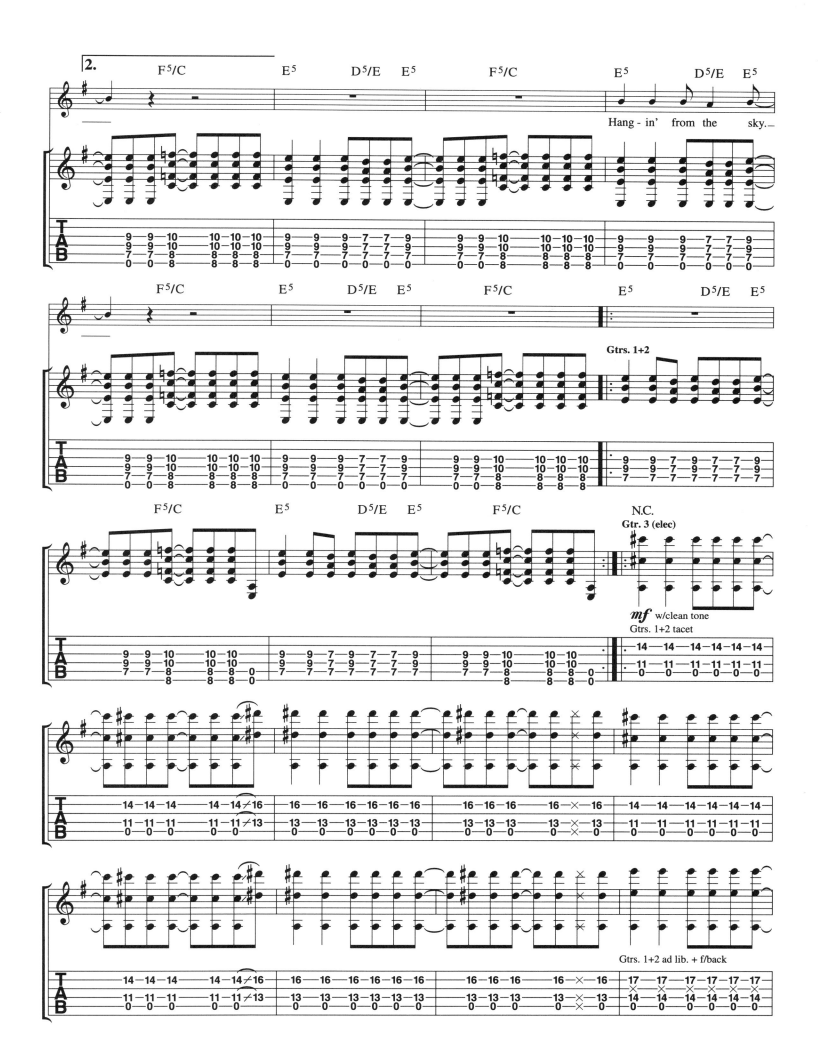

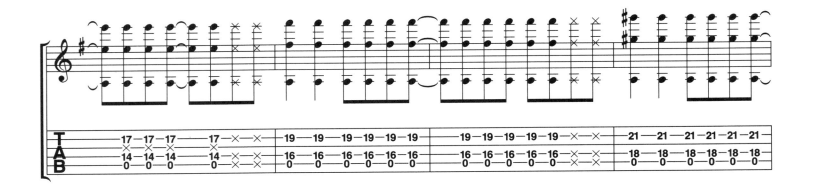

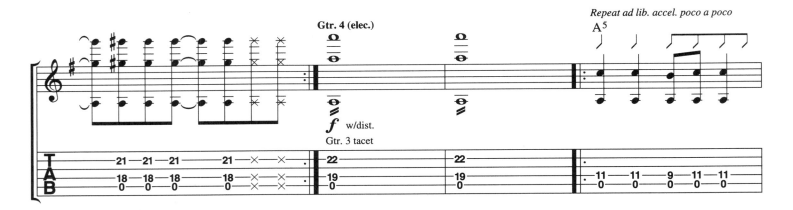

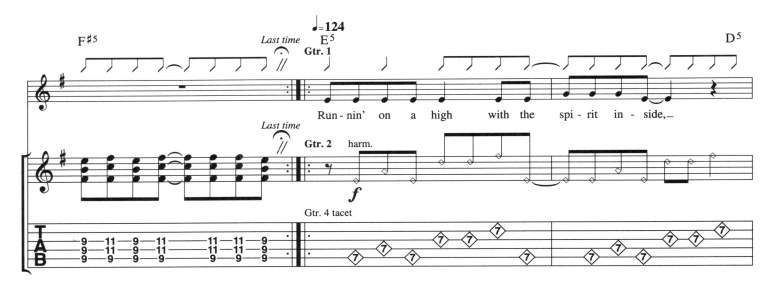

Run - nin' on a high with the spi - rit in - side,

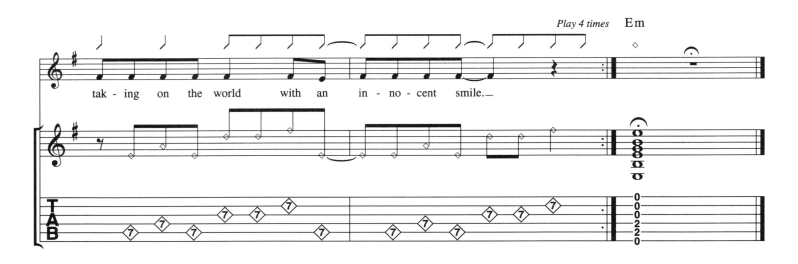

tak - ing on the world with an in - no - cent smile.

Darkside Lightside

Words & Music by Tim Wheeler

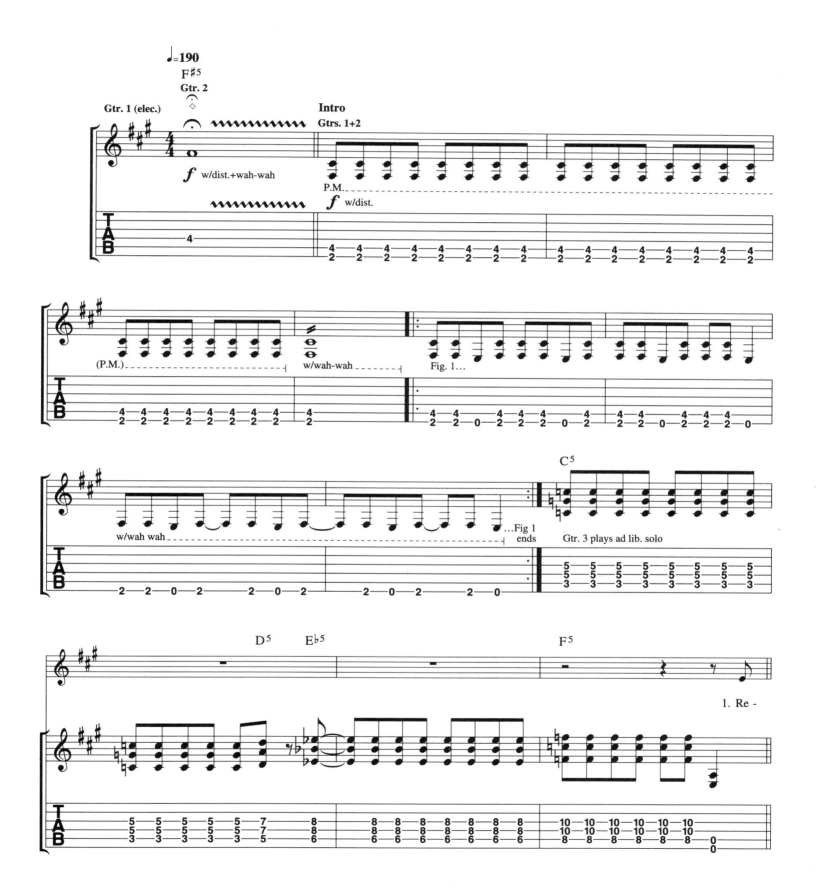

that I had for-got.___ I get the feel-ings that I used to get___

___ and re-mem-ber things___ that I had for-get-ten long a-go.___

Exclusive Distributors:
Music Sales Limited
8/9 Frith Street, London W1V 5TZ, England.
Music Sales Pty Limited
120 Rothschild Avenue, Rosebery, NSW 2018, Australia.

Order No.AM944625
ISBN 0-7119-6664-8
This book © Copyright 1997 by
Island Music Limited

Visit the Internet Music Shop at
http://www.musicsales.co.uk

Music arranged by Martin Shellard.
Music processed by Paul Ewers Music Design.

Printed in the United Kingdom by
Halstan & Co Limited, Amersham, Buckinghamshire.

Your Guarantee of Quality:
As publishers, we strive to produce every book to the
highest commercial standards. The music has been freshly
engraved and, whilst endeavouring to retain the original
running order of the recorded album, the book has been
carefully designed to minimise awkward page turns and to
make playing from it a real pleasure. Particular care has been
given to specifying acid-free, neutral-sized paper made from
pulps which have not been elemental chlorine bleached.
This pulp is from farmed sustainable forests and was
produced with special regard for the environment.
Throughout, the printing and binding have been planned to
ensure a sturdy, attractive publication which should give years
of enjoyment. If your copy fails to meet our high standards,
please inform us and we will gladly replace it.

Music Sales' complete catalogue describes
thousands of titles and is available in full colour
sections by subject, direct from Music Sales Limited.
Please state your areas of interest and send
a cheque/postal order for £1.50 for postage to:
Music Sales Limited, Newmarket Road, Bury St. Edmunds,
Suffolk IP33 3YB.